20

The Get Up and Go D

ISBN 978-1-9

Do not stop thinking of life as an adventure.
You have no security unless you can live bravely,
excitingly, imaginatively; unless you can choose
a challenge instead of competence.
Eleanor Roosevelt

GetUpandGo

Published in Ireland by
GET UP AND GO PUBLICATIONS LTD
Camboline, Hazelwood, Sligo, F91 NP04, Ireland.
Email: info@getupandgodiary.com
www.getupandgodiary.com

Compiled by Eileen Forrestal
Graphic design by Nuala Redmond
Illustrations: dreamstime.com; shutterstock.com
Printed in Ireland by GPS Colour Graphics.

2023 BANK AND PUBLIC HOLIDAYS

REPUBLIC OF IRELAND
New Year's Day, 2 January;
St Patrick's Day, 17 March;
Easter Monday, 10 April;
June Bank Holiday, 5 June;
October Bank Holiday, 30 October;
St Stephen's Day, 26 December.

St Brigid's Day, 6 February
Good Friday, 7 April;
May Day Bank Holiday, 1 May;
August Bank Holiday, 7 August;
Christmas Day, 25 December;

NORTHERN IRELAND
New Year's Day, 2 January;
Good Friday, 7 April;
May Day Holiday, 1 May;
Orangemen's Holiday, 12 July;
Christmas Day, 25 December;

St Patrick's Day, 17 March;
Easter Monday, 10 April;
Spring Bank Holiday, 29 May;
Summer Bank Holiday, 28 August;
Boxing Day, 26 December.

ENGLAND, SCOTLAND AND WALES
New Year's Day, 2 January;
Easter Monday, 10 April;
May Day Holiday, 1 May;
Summer Bank Holiday, 28 August;
Christmas Day, 25 December;

Good Friday, 7 April;
St George's Day, 23 April
Spring Bank Holiday, 29 May;
Remembrance Sunday, 12 November;
Boxing Day, 26 December.

UNITED STATES OF AMERICA
New Year's Day, 2 January;
Presidents' Day, 20 February;
Independence Day, 4 July;
Columbus Day, 9 October;
Thanksgiving Day, 23 November;

Martin Luther King Day, 16 January;
Memorial Day, 29 May;
Labour Day, 4 September;
Veterans Day, 10 November;
Christmas Day, 25 December.

CANADA
New Year's Day, 2 January;
Heritage Day, 20 February;
St Patrick's Day, 17 March;
Easter Monday, 10 April;
Canada Day, 1 July;
Thanksgiving Day, 9 October;
Christmas Day, 25 December;

Family Day, 20 February;
Commonwealth Day, 13 March;
Good Friday, 7 April;
Victoria Day 22 May;
Labour Day, 4 September;
Rememberance Day, 11 November;
Boxing Day, 26 December.

AUSTRALIA (NATIONAL HOLIDAYS)
New Year's Day, 2 January;
Good Friday, 7 April;
Anzac Day 25 April;
Christmas Day, 25 December;

Australia Day, 26 January;
Easter Monday, 10 April;
Queen's Birthday, 12 June;
Boxing Day, 26 December.

2023

JANUARY

SUN	MON	TUE	WED	THU	FRI	SAT
1	2	3	4	5	6	7
8	9	10	11	12	13	14
15	16	17	18	19	20	21
22	23	24	25	26	27	28
29	30	31				

FEBRUARY

SUN	MON	TUE	WED	THU	FRI	SAT
			1	2	3	4
5	6	7	8	9	10	11
12	13	14	15	16	17	18
19	20	21	22	23	24	25
26	27	28				

MARCH

SUN	MON	TUE	WED	THU	FRI	SAT
			1	2	3	4
5	6	7	8	9	10	11
12	13	14	15	16	17	18
19	20	21	22	23	24	25
26	27	28	29	30	31	

APRIL

SUN	MON	TUE	WED	THU	FRI	SAT
						1
2	3	4	5	6	7	8
9	10	11	12	13	14	15
16	17	18	19	20	21	22
23	24	25	26	27	28	29
30						

MAY

SUN	MON	TUE	WED	THU	FRI	SAT
	1	2	3	4	5	6
7	8	9	10	11	12	13
14	15	16	17	18	19	20
21	22	23	24	25	26	27
28	29	30	31			

JUNE

SUN	MON	TUE	WED	THU	FRI	SAT
				1	2	3
4	5	6	7	8	9	10
11	12	13	14	15	16	17
18	19	20	21	22	23	24
25	26	27	28	29	30	

JULY

SUN	MON	TUE	WED	THU	FRI	SAT
						1
2	3	4	5	6	7	8
9	10	11	12	13	14	15
16	17	18	19	20	21	22
23	24	25	26	27	28	29
30	31					

AUGUST

SUN	MON	TUE	WED	THU	FRI	SAT
		1	2	3	4	5
6	7	8	9	10	11	12
13	14	15	16	17	18	19
20	21	22	23	24	25	26
27	28	29	30	31		

SEPTEMBER

SUN	MON	TUE	WED	THU	FRI	SAT
					1	2
3	4	5	6	7	8	9
10	11	12	13	14	15	16
17	18	19	20	21	22	23
24	25	26	27	28	29	30

OCTOBER

SUN	MON	TUE	WED	THU	FRI	SAT
1	2	3	4	5	6	7
8	9	10	11	12	13	14
15	16	17	18	19	20	21
22	23	24	25	26	27	28
29	30	31				

NOVEMBER

SUN	MON	TUE	WED	THU	FRI	SAT
			1	2	3	4
5	6	7	8	9	10	11
12	13	14	15	16	17	18
19	20	21	22	23	24	25
26	27	28	29	30		

DECEMBER

SUN	MON	TUE	WED	THU	FRI	SAT
					1	2
3	4	5	6	7	8	9
10	11	12	13	14	15	16
17	18	19	20	21	22	23
24	25	26	27	28	29	30
31						

Forgive the past – let it go
Live the present – the power of now
Create the future – thoughts become things

Dear Reader,

We are delighted that you're holding this Get Up and Go diary in your hands today. You are about to embark on a wonderful journey with 'the world's best loved transformational diary'.

Whether this is your first Get Up and Go diary or you're a regular and loyal customer, we thank you, and we trust that you will benefit from the carefully chosen words contained herein.

You may have chosen this diary for yourself or received it as gift from a friend; either way, we know it will fill your days with inspiration, encouragement, motivation and empowerment in the year ahead.

You may also like to follow us on Facebook, Twitter and Instagram for additional timely words of inspiration and encouragement. Please check out our website **www.getupandgodiary.com** where you can find out about (and purchase) new products, follow our blog, **subscribe to our newsletter**, learn about upcoming events and see details of special offers.

Also there's something extra we think you'll appreciate. Through our partnership with the Global Giving Initiative **www.B1G1.com** this diary is changing lives – a contribution from each diary becomes a 'Giving Impact' in support of a worthy cause in the developing world. You'll see more about all of that on our website.

And it all happens because people like you love their Get Up and Go diary. Thank you so much for being one of them.

We are delighted to say we are now sourcing our paper from FSC. FSC certification ensures that products come from responsibly managed forests that provide environmental, social and economic benefits. And ... we have been named "Allstar Inspirational Diary of the Year"!

Thank you for your support.

With very best wishes for the year ahead,

from the Get Up and Go team

This diary belongs to: _____

Address: _____

Tel: _____ Email: _____

Emergency telephone number: _____

BUCKET LIST for January

Courage MONTH

Ok, so you noticed the day and the date on the calendar changed!

What are you going to change today... to make the calendar notice?

We will open the book. Its pages are blank. We are going to put words on them ourselves. The book is called *Opportunity* and its first chapter is New Year's Day.

Edith Lovejoy Pierce

January

The problem with making New Year
resolutions in January ... is January!
It's a winter month.
Winter is a time for reflection.
We are still resting. Relax.
This is your reward for a year well lived.
Breathe. Let your mind settle.
Use this reflective time to look back on a busy year that's
gone and look forward to the empty one ahead.
Plan to fill it with whatever enriches your experience of life.
You need not make any resolutions until February when you
can tap into the Spring energy – for new growth to bring new
solutions to old problems. Seeds are still germinating in Winter
waiting to be planted out in fertile soil in Spring so they
can flower in Summer and be harvested in Autumn.
Winter will come round again.

*Adopt the pace of nature. Nothing is
rushed and all is accomplished.*

Lao Tzu

Be willing to be
a beginner every
single morning.

Meister Eckhart

GOOD
MORNING

SUNDAY **1** HAPPY NEW YEAR!

Trust yourself first

Be willing to let go of a losing strategy

Success comes with persistence, and patience

We cannot discover new oceans until we have courage to lose sight of the shore.
Andre Gide

RULES OF LIFE TO GET YOU GOING

1. Make peace with your past, so it won't screw up your future.
2. What others think of you is less important than what you think of them.
3. Time heals almost everything. Give time time – and a wee push when necessary.
4. Avoid the pitfall of comparing your life with others- they are on their own journey.
5. Thinking is good. Over thinking is not better. Action is best. Action gets results.
6. Don't put the key to your happiness in someone else's pocket.
7. Smile. It lights up your eyes and brightens up the view.

January

The older you get, the better you get.
Unless you're a banana.
Betty White

WEDNESDAY 4

Do your best with what you have

THURSDAY 5

Create balance in your mind and bring it to your life

FRIDAY 6

Playing small does not serve the world

SATURDAY 7

Develop self-reliance

SUNDAY 8

Practice attentive listening

Change is the only constant in life.
Heraclitus

MONDAY 9

Have the courage to fight for what you believe in

TUESDAY 10

Nothing positive comes from worry

The risk to remain tight in the bud was more painful than the risk it took to blossom.
Anais Nin

Very often a change of self is needed, rather than a change of scene; a point of view rather than the view itself. To live is to change. To be perfect is to have changed often.
John Henry Newman

You need not remain in bondage to your first experience, your first relationship, your first version of yourself ... but you must remain in homage to the highest vision of yourself.

WEDNESDAY 11

Keep your environment clean and tidy

January

Every small positive change we make in ourselves repays us in confidence in the future.
Alice Walker

Keep smiling, because life is a beautiful thing and there's so much to smile about.
Marilyn Monroe

THURSDAY **12**

Choose freely and accept the consequences

FRIDAY **13**

Life is a balancing act

SATURDAY **14**

Discover your Why and the How will take care of itself

SUNDAY **15**

Whatever game you're playing, be a good sport!

For a long time it had seemed to me that life was about to begin – real life. But there was always some obstacle in the way, something to be gotten through first, some unfinished business, time still to be served, or a debt to be paid. Then life would begin. At last it dawned on me that these obstacles were my life.

Alfred D Souza

Believe that life is worth living and you and your belief will help you create a life worth living. Trust that life is worth loving and you and your trust will help you create a life worth loving. Love that life is worth living and loving and you and your love will help you create a life worth loving and living.

Don't ask what the world needs. Ask yourself what makes you come alive and go do that. What the world needs is people who have come alive.

Howard Thurman

MONDAY **16**

Develop your leadership skills

TUESDAY **17**

Stuff happens, it's not personal

Patience is always rewarded and romance is always round the corner!

Ayn Rand

WEDNESDAY **18**

Don't take anything, or anyone, for granted

THURSDAY **19**

Have a laugh with your friends

FRIDAY **20**

Random complaining is unproductive

SATURDAY **21**

Do what needs to be done

SUNDAY **22**

Find someone to hug, and hug them

OUR DEEPEST FEAR

Our deepest fear is not that we are inadequate.
Our deepest fear is that we are powerful beyond measure.
It is our light not our darkness that most frightens us.
We ask ourselves – who am I to be brilliant,
gorgeous, talented and fabulous?
Actually who are you not to be?
You are a child of God.
Your playing small does not serve the world.
There's nothing enlightened about shrinking
so that other people won't feel insecure around you.
We were born to make manifest the glory of God that is within us.
It's not just in some of us, it's in everyone
And as we let our own light shine
We unconsciously give other people permission to do the same.
As we are liberated from our own fears
Our presence automatically liberates others.

Marianne Williamson

I'm 36 and I have so many unanswered questions!!!!
I still haven't found out who let the Dogs Out ... How to get to
Sesame Street... Why Dora doesn't just use Google Maps ... Why do
all flavours of fruit loops taste exactly the same, How do they get the
figs into the fig rolls ... Why does Donald Duck wear a towel after a
shower yet never wears pants .... Why are eggs packaged in a flimsy
paper carton, but batteries are secured in plastic that's tough as
nails, and light bulbs are also in a flimsy box ..
What about scissors? You need scissors to cut into the
packaging of scissors ...
I still don't understand why there is Braille on drive up ATM's or why
"abbreviated" is such a long word, or why is there a D in 'fridge'
but not in refrigerator... or why lemon juice is made with artificial
flavour yet dish-washing liquid is made with real lemons ... or why
they sterilize the needle for lethal injections ... and, why do you have
to "put your two cents in" but it's only a "penny for your thoughts"
(where's that extra penny going to??) ... why do The Alphabet Song
and Twinkle Twinkle Little Star have the same tune ...
and why did I just try to sing those two songs ...??
There are so many unanswered questions in life.

January

MONDAY 23

Have a daily to do list

TUESDAY 24

Imagine life from another's perspective

WEDNESDAY 25

You can't please everyone

THURSDAY 26

Contribute to a better way

Loneliness does not come from having no people around us, but from being unable to communicate the things that are important to us, to the people around us.

Wanting to be someone else is a
waste of the person you are.

Marilyn Monroe

*A friend is one who joyfully
sings with you when you are
on the mountaintop, and
silently walks beside you
through the valley.*

William Arthur Ward

We can be resentful of our age, or we can
be grateful for having attained it.

William Arthur Ward

**Being a woman is
a terribly difficult
task, since it consists
principally in dealing
with men.**

Joseph Conrad

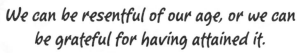

Be careful what you water your dreams with.
Water them with worry and fear and you
will produce weeds that choke the life
from your dream. Water them with
optimism and you will cultivate success.
Always be on the lookout for ways
to turn a problem into an opportunity.
Always be on the lookout for ways
to nurture your dream.

Lao Tzu

*Life isn't as serious as our mind
sometimes makes it out to be.*

January

If we don't change, we don't grow. If we don't grow, we aren't really living.

Anatole France

Reach high, for stars lie hidden in your soul. Dream deep, for every dream precedes a goal.

Rabindranath Tagore

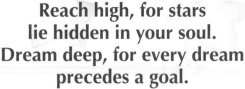

To have courage for whatever comes in life, everything lies in that.

St Teresa of Avila

FRIDAY 27

Maybe 'having it all' is not the goal

SATURDAY 28

Empower children to be responsible adults

SUNDAY 29

Compliment when a compliment is due

MONDAY **30**

Aspire to excellence

TUESDAY **31**

You can't achieve greatness by yourself

Hope ever urges us on and tells us tomorrow will be better.

Albius Tibullus

In everyone's life, at some time, our inner fire goes out. It is then burst into flame by an encounter with another human being. We should all be thankful for those people who rekindle the inner spirit.

Albert Schweitzer

Every child comes into the world with the message that God does not yet despair of man.

Rabindranath Tagore

17

BUCKET LIST
for
February

Love MONTH

_____
_____
_____
_____
_____
_____
_____
_____
_____
_____
_____
_____
_____
_____
_____
_____
_____
_____
_____

*Love yourself first and everything
else falls into line. You really have
to love yourself to get anything
done in this world.*
Lucille Ball

*Love for the joy of loving, and not for the
offerings of someone else's heart.*
Marlene Dietrich

I've fallen in love. I'm an ordinary woman.
I didn't think such violent things could happen
to ordinary people.

**Feeling sorry for yourself,
and your present condition,
is not only a waste of energy
but the worst habit you
could possibly have.**

Dale Carnegie

*Life shrinks or
expands in proportion
to one's courage.*

Anais Nin

WEDNESDAY **1**

Organise yourself to reduce stress

THURSDAY **2**

Avoid people who bring you down

FRIDAY **3**

Clear decisions make life easier

SATURDAY **4**

Your body hears everything your mind says

February

A SMILE

It costs nothing, but creates much.
It enriches those who receive, without impoverishing those who give.
It happens in a flash and the memory of it sometimes lasts forever.
None are so rich they can get along without it and none so poor but are richer for its benefits.
It creates happiness in the home, fosters goodwill in a business, and is the countersign of friends.
It is rest to the weary, daylight to the discouraged, sunshine to the sad, and nature's best antidote for trouble.
Yet it cannot be bought, begged, borrowed or stolen, for it is something that is no earthly good to anyone 'til it is given away. And if in the hurly-burly bustle of today's business world, some of the people you meet should be too tired to give you a smile, may we ask you to leave one of yours?
For nobody needs a smile so much as those who have none left to give.

Dale Carnegie

Cosmopolitan cocktail

WHAT YOU WILL NEED
45ml lemon vodka
15ml triple sec
30ml cranberry juice
10ml lime juice
Ice

THE HOW-TO PART
Shake ingredients with ice and strain into a cocktail glass. Garnish with orange zest or a lime wedge on the rim of the glass

SUNDAY **5**

Choose to respond not to react

PRETTY *UGLY?*

I am very ugly
So don't try to convince me that
I am a very beautiful person
Because at the end of the day
I hate myself in every single way
And I'm not going to lie to myself by saying
There is a beauty inside me that matters
So rest assured I will remind myself
That I am a worthless, terrible person
And nothing you say will make me believe
I still deserve love
Because no matter what
I am not good enough to be loved
And I am in no position to believe that
Beauty does exists inside me
Because whenever I look in the mirror I always think
Am I as ugly as people say?
(Now read from the bottom up ....)
    Abdullah Shoaib

Beauty begins the moment you decide to be yourself.

Coco Chanel

We do not need magic to transform our world. We carry all of the power we need inside ourselves already.

JK Rowling

We may not have it all together, but together we can have it all.

February

But I found love when I was with myself.
I went with nature, with animals, and I found
love and harmony. I would come home at the end
of the day – braids pulled out, my dress torn – and
of course I got asked 'where have you been all day?'
But I had been in a world of love and happiness.

Tina Turner

MONDAY 6 Bank holiday

Stay true to your purpose

TUESDAY 7

Invest in yourself

WEDNESDAY 8

Give yourself permission to go for what you really want

THURSDAY 9

Be a trailblazer

FRIDAY **10**

Don't sell yourself short

With the new day comes new strength and new thoughts.
Eleanor Roosevelt

If we listened to our intellect, we'd never have a love affair. We'd never have a friendship. We'd never go into business because we'd be too cynical. Well, that's nonsense. You've got to jump off cliffs all the time and build your wings on the way down.
Annie Dillard

When dealing with people, remember you are not dealing with creatures of logic, but creatures of emotion.
Dale Carnegie

SATURDAY **11**

Acknowledge your bad habits

SUNDAY **12**

Don't worry about it being perfect, just get it started

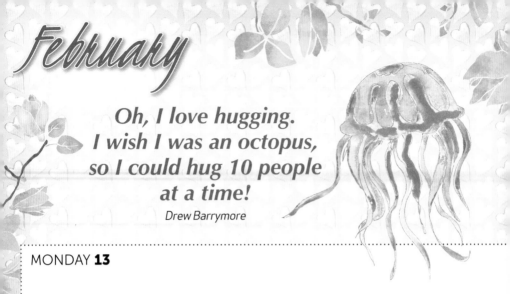

February

*Oh, I love hugging.
I wish I was an octopus,
so I could hug 10 people
at a time!*

Drew Barrymore

MONDAY 13

Give the gift of your happiness to your friends and family

TUESDAY 14   St Valentine's Day

Have a mind open to new ideas

WEDNESDAY 15

Don't wait – the time will never be just right

THURSDAY 16

There are unlimited possibilities inside you

10 BUILDING BLOCKS OF CONFIDENCE

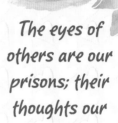

Curiosity.
Spontaneity.
Enthusiasm.
Happiness.
Courage.
Adventure.
Self belief.
Trust.
Love
Joy.

The eyes of others are our prisons; their thoughts our cages.

Virginia Woolfe

I came here tonight because when you realise you want to spend the rest of your life with somebody, you want the rest of your life to start as soon as possible.

When Harry met Sally

Hatred is a negative passion. It is powerful – a very powerful destroyer; but it is useless for building up. Love on the other hand is like faith; it can move mountains, and faith, we have mountains to move.

Douglas Hyde

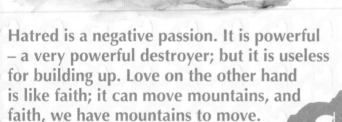

We need to reshape our own perception of how we view ourselves. We have to step up as women and take the lead.

Beyoncé

February

Time will explain.
Jane Austen

FRIDAY 17

Be ok with uncertainty

SATURDAY 18

We all have the capacity for recuperation and repair

SUNDAY 19

All is well

Some people care too much. I think it's called love.
Winnie the Pooh

Don't hold on to someone who's leaving, otherwise you won't meet the one who's coming.

If you love someone you say it, you say it right there and then, out loud. Otherwise, the moment just … passes you by.

I like not only to be loved, but also to be told
that I am loved. I am not sure that you are of the same
mind. But the realm of silence is large enough beyond
the grave. This is the world of light and speech,
and I shall take leave to tell you
that you are very dear.

George Eliot

Though we travel the world over
to find the beautiful, we must carry
it with us, or we find it not.

Ralph Waldo Emerson

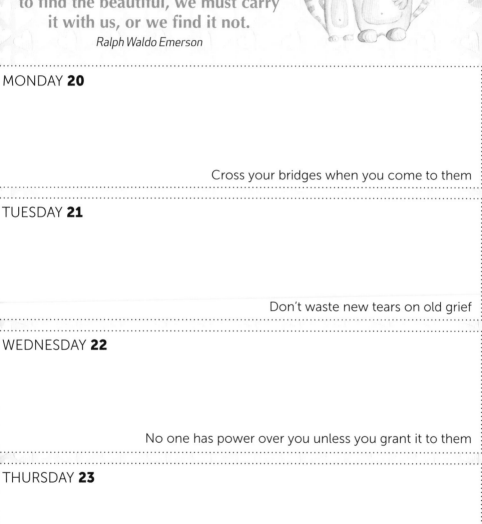

MONDAY **20**

Cross your bridges when you come to them

TUESDAY **21**

Don't waste new tears on old grief

WEDNESDAY **22**

No one has power over you unless you grant it to them

THURSDAY **23**

Take care not to stagnate in your comfort zone

February

A woman has to live her
life, or live to repent not
having lived it.

DH Lawrence

FRIDAY 24

Where you arrive is where it begins

SATURDAY 25

Differences enrich families

SUNDAY 26

Master your habits or you will be their slave

You become.
It takes a long time.
That's why it doesn't happen often to people
who break easily, or have sharp edges,
or who have to be carefully kept.
Generally, by the time you are Real,
most of your hair has been loved off, and your
eyes drop out and you get loose in your
joints and very shabby. But these things
don't matter at all, because once you are Real
you can't be ugly, except to people
who don't understand.

Margery Williams Bianco, The Velveteen Rabbit

MONDAY **27**

Don't just go through life, grow and glow with life

TUESDAY **28**

Don't complicate your life with fears and doubts

LOVE

The time will come when, with elation,
you will greet yourself arriving at your own door,
in your own mirror, and each will smile at the
other's welcome, and say, sit here. Eat.
You will love again the stranger who was your self.
Give back your heart to itself, to the stranger who
has loved you all your life, who knows you by
heart, whom you ignored for another.
Take down the love letters from the
bookshelf, the photographs, peel
your own image from the mirror.
Sit. Feast on your life.

from Derek Walcott

At the touch of love
everyone becomes a poet.

Plato

Love and kindness are never wasted. They always
make a difference. They bless the one who receives
them, and they bless you, the giver.

Barbara De Angelis

29

BUCKET LIST

for
March

Friendship MONTH

It's often just enough to be with someone. You don't need to touch them. Not even talk. A feeling passes between you both. You're not alone.

Marilyn Monroe

A friend is one who joyfully sings with you when you are on the mountaintop, and silently walks beside you through the valley.

William Arthur Ward

12 LEVELS OF FRIENDSHIP

1) A nodding acquaintance – friendly greeting.
2) A colleague / shared interests or community.
3) Someone you are comfortable sitting with for a short time.
4) You enjoy a good conversation.
5) A social companion you might call when you're free for coffee/tea/beer.
6) They express concern for your wellbeing – and you for theirs.
7) You can depend on – someone you can go on holiday with.
8) True friend. No ulterior motive.
9) A close intimate friend in whose presence you feel calm and happy.
10) A confidant – someone you can comfortably trust with your inner life.
11) Your best friend – one you have chosen above all others.
12) You are inseparable. Soul mates.

From Arabic

In the sweetness of friendship let there be laughter, and sharing of pleasures. For in the dew of little things the heart finds its morning and is refreshed.

Khalil Gibran

WEDNESDAY 1

Take care of your body – it's the only place you live

THURSDAY 2

Time is a great healer; give time time

March

I am a work in progress...
I'm strong because I have been weak.
I'm brave because I have been afraid.
I'm smart because I have been stupid.
I'm wise because I have been foolish.
I'm healing because I have been hurt.
I'm old because I have been young.

Ah! The strength of women comes from the fact that psychology cannot explain us. Science can never grapple with the irrational.
Oscar Wilde

FRIDAY 3

You can always find something positive to say

SATURDAY 4

To get unstuck, do something, anything!

SUNDAY 5

Make an intentional effort to slow down

It is not the perfect, but the imperfect, who have need of love.

MONDAY 6

Honour your parents

So whether they've been a friend
for 20 minutes or 20+ years,
express your gratitude for the women
that God has placed in your life.
They make a difference for you.
And you make a difference for them.

Forgiveness is a funny thing.
It warms the heart and cools the sting.

The more we count the blessings we have,
the less we crave the luxuries we do not have.

William Arthur Ward

TUESDAY 7

Get interested in other people

March

WEDNESDAY 8

Ask for advice and listen to it

THURSDAY 9

Welcome the perspective of others

FRIDAY 10

Don't overthink it

SATURDAY 11

When you mess up, 'fess up

SUNDAY 12

Everyone has hidden struggles

When I was a little girl,
I believed in the concept of one best friend.
As I became a woman,
I discovered that if we allow our heart to open up,
we will find the best in many friends.
One friend is needed when we're going through things with our men.
Another friend is needed when we're going through things
with our moms.
Another will sit beside us in the bleachers as we delight in our
children and their activities.
Another when we want to shop, share, heal, hurt, joke, or just be.
One friend will say, 'Let's cry together'.
Another , 'Let's laugh together'.
Another , 'Let's walk and talk together'.
One friend will meet our spiritual needs,
Another our shoe fetish,
Another our love for movies,
Another will be with us in our season of confusion or loss,
Another will be our confidante and clarifier,
Another the wind beneath our wings.
But whatever their assignment in our life,
On whatever the occasion,
On whatever the day,
Or wherever we need them to meet us with their
running shoes on and their hair pulled back,
Or to hold us back from making a complete fool of ourselves.
Or picking up the pieces when we do,
These are our best friends.
It may all be wrapped up in one person,
but for many, it's wrapped up
in several…
… from 7th grade,
… from high school,
… from college years,
… from old jobs.
On some days it's our mother.
On some days it's our sister.
On some days it's our colleague or boss.
On some days it's our neighbour.
On some days it's our daughter.

March

**Happiness is not a goal...
it's a by-product of a life well lived.**

Eleanor Roosevelt

MONDAY 13

Eat well, your body will thank you

TUESDAY 14

Be ok with imperfections

WEDNESDAY 15

Celebrate all that is good in your life

THURSDAY 16

If you are overburdened, delegate!

FRIDAY 17 Bank holiday

🍀 St Patricks Day

If you want to fly, you have to give up what weighs you down.

SATURDAY **18**

Give credit where credit is due

SUNDAY **19** Mother's Day

Keep your thoughts to yourself

Yesterday is but a dream. Tomorrow is only a vision. But today well lived makes every yesterday a dream of happiness, and every tomorrow a vision of hope.

Kālidāsa

But let there be spaces in your togetherness and let the winds of the heavens dance between you. Love one another but make not a bond of love: let it rather be a moving sea between the shores of your souls.

Khalil Gibran

March

Most of us have far more courage than we ever dreamed we possessed.

Dale Carnegie

Do not train a child to learn by force or harshness; but direct them to it by what amuses their minds, so that you may be better able to discover with accuracy the peculiar bent of the genius of each.

Plato

MONDAY 20

It's ok to ask for help

TUESDAY 21

Challenge yourself to learn a new skill

WEDNESDAY 22

Don't neglect your responsibilities

THURSDAY 23

Be open to discovering something new

FRIDAY **24**

Thinking is overrated

SATURDAY **25**

Be grateful for all the good things in your life.

SUNDAY **26**

This is not a dress rehearsal

Whatever career you may choose for yourself – doctor, lawyer, teacher – let me propose an avocation to be pursued along with it. Become a dedicated fighter for civil rights. Make it a central part of your life. It will make you a better doctor, a better lawyer, a better teacher. It will enrich your spirit as nothing else possibly can. It will give you that rare sense of nobility that can only spring from love and selflessly helping your fellow man. Make a career of humanity. Commit yourself to the noble struggle for human rights. You will make a greater person of yourself, a greater nation of your country and a finer world to live in.

Martin Luther King Jr

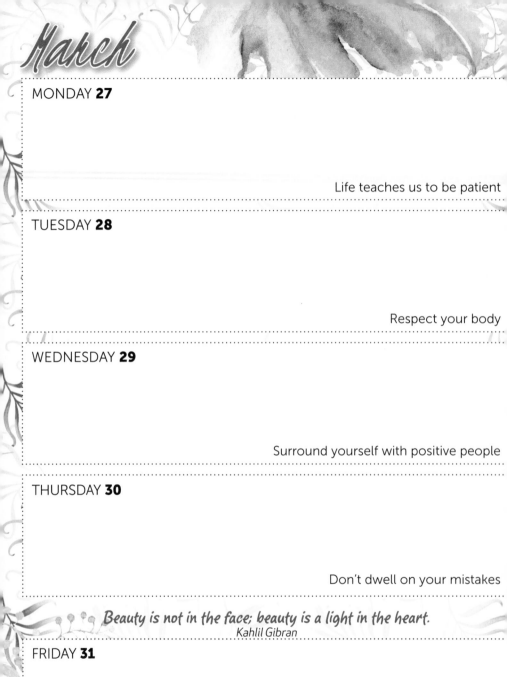

March

MONDAY 27

Life teaches us to be patient

TUESDAY 28

Respect your body

WEDNESDAY 29

Surround yourself with positive people

THURSDAY 30

Don't dwell on your mistakes

Beauty is not in the face; beauty is a light in the heart.
Kahlil Gibran

FRIDAY 31

Acknowledge your accomplishments

BUCKET LIST

for April

Creativity MONTH

I don't intend to shrink from the truth,
because the longer it's postponed, the harder it will be
for them to accept it when they do hear it!
Anne Frank

SATURDAY **1**

Be who you really are

April

CHILDREN LEARN WHAT THEY LIVE

If children live with criticism, they learn to *condemn.*
If children live with hostility, they learn to *fight.*
If children live with fear, they learn to be *apprehensive.*
If children live with pity, they learn to feel *sorry for themselves.*
If children live with ridicule, they learn to feel *shy.*
If children live with jealousy, they learn to feel *envy.*
If children live with shame, they learn to feel *guilty.*

If children live with encouragement, they learn *confidence.*
If children live with tolerance, they learn *patience.*
If children live with praise, they learn *appreciation.*
If children live with acceptance, they learn to *love.*
If children live with approval, they learn to *like themselves.*
If children live with recognition, they learn it is *good to have a goal.*
If children live with sharing, they learn *generosity.*
If children live with honesty, they learn *truthfulness.*
If children live with fairness, they learn *justice.*
If children live with kindness and consideration, they learn *respect.*
If children live with security, they learn to have *faith in themselves and in those about them.*
If children live with friendliness, they learn that *the world is a nice place in which to live.*

> Dorothy Law Nolte

When we seek to discover the best in others, we somehow bring out the best in ourselves.

> William Arthur Ward

SUNDAY **2**

Take care of yourself

What counts, in the long run, is not what you read; it is the ideas and impressions that are aroused in you by your reading. It is the ideas stirred in your own mind, the ideas which are a reflection of your own thinking, which make you an interesting person.

Eleanor Roosevelt

The greatest mistake physicians make is that they attempt to cure the body without attempting to cure the mind; yet the mind and the body are one and should not be treated separately!

Plato

MONDAY 3

You are good, you belong and you are not alone

TUESDAY 4

Critics are everywhere; beware the one between your ears

WEDNESDAY 5

Forgive yourself, forgive others

THURSDAY 6

Celebrate the 'little wins'

April

A bad habit never disappears on its own; it's an 'Undo -It -Yourself' project.

The biggest changes in a women's nature are brought by love; in man, by ambition.

Tagore, Rabindranath

One loyal friend is worth ten thousand relatives.

Euripides

Behaviour is the mirror in which everyone shows their image.

Goethe

FRIDAY 7 Good Friday

Collaborate where possible

SATURDAY 8

Love your job ... or leave

SUNDAY 9 Easter Sunday

Expand your dreams to live your fullest life

This world demands the qualities of youth:
not a time of life but a state of mind,
a temper of the will, a quality of imagination,
a predominance of courage over
timidity, of the appetite for
adventure over the love of ease.

Robert F Kennedy

MONDAY 10 Easter Monday

Trust your intuition

TUESDAY 11

Value your own opinions

WEDNESDAY 12

Allow yourself to give more than is expected of you

THURSDAY 13

There is nothing to be gained by putting yourself down

April

Someone I loved once gave me a box full of darkness. It took me years to understand that this too, was a gift.

Mary Oliver

The great advantage about telling the truth is that nobody ever believes it.

Dorothy L Sayers

It is not so much our friends' help that helps us, as the confidence of their help.

Epicurus

FRIDAY 14

Let go of the need to control

SATURDAY 15

Don't let your fears hold you back

SUNDAY 16

You are in charge of the thoughts you think

If you cry because the sun has gone out of your life, your tears will prevent you from seeing the stars.

Tagore

We can easily forgive a child who is afraid of the dark; the real tragedy of life is when men are afraid of the light.

Plato

If I can't make it through one door, I'll go through another door – or I'll make a door. Something terrific will come no matter how dark the present.

Rabindranath Tagore

Our sins are more easily remembered than our good deeds.

Democritus

MONDAY 17

It takes courage to choose to change

TUESDAY 18

Don't make assumptions

WEDNESDAY 19

Give up the struggle and dance with life

April

Every day we should hear at least one little song, read one good poem, see one exquisite picture, and, if possible, speak a few sensible words.

Johann Wolfgang von Goethe

I think one's feelings waste themselves in words, they ought all to be distilled into actions and into actions which bring results.

Florence Nightingale

THURSDAY 20

Take control of your financial situation

FRIDAY 21

Don't just chat, connect.

SATURDAY 22

Believe anything is possible

SUNDAY 23

Have a bath by candlelight

MONDAY **24**

Encourage others

TUESDAY **25**

Don't buy the lie

I long to accomplish a great and noble task, but it is my chief duty to accomplish humble tasks as though they were great and noble. The world is moved along, not only by the mighty shoves of its heroes, but also by the aggregate of the tiny pushes of each honest worker.
Helen Keller

Never doubt that a small group of thoughtful, committed, citizens can change the world. Indeed, it is the only thing that ever has.
Margaret Mead

There is a crack in everything.
That's how the light gets in.
Leonard Cohen

A good marriage is the union of two good forgivers.
Mark Twain

Life is under no obligation to give us what we expect.

Margaret Mitchell

WEDNESDAY 26

Brainstorm with your friends and family

THURSDAY 27

Keep a journal

FRIDAY 28

Crystallise your desires into words and actions

SATURDAY 29

Do what you say

SUNDAY 30

You can leave the past behind

BUCKET LIST

for May

Happiness MONTH

> I choose to be happy because its good for my health.
> *Voltaire*

> One must dare to be happy.
> *Gertrude Stein*

_____
_____
_____
_____
_____
_____
_____
_____
_____
_____
_____
_____
_____
_____

A warm smile is the universal language of kindness.

William Arthur Ward

I'm a big believer that if you choose happiness, then success will follow. Happiness encourages good life decisions, bolsters wonderful relationships, and opens up doors to great opportunities.

HELPFUL HINTS ON HAPPINESS

There is no way to happiness. Happiness is the way.
Be true to your higher self. Be a happy human being.
Happiness is a function of accepting what is,
and letting go of what 'should not' be.
You are good enough just as you are.
Breathe and relax in the happiness of this thought.
People are usually as happy as they make up their minds to be.
Very little is needed to be happy in life. Choose to be happy.
Happiness is when what you think, what you say and what you
do are in harmony.
It is all within yourself, in your attitude and your way of thinking.
Happiness comes through doors you didn't even know were open.
Make space for happiness in your day.
Clear out what's in the way, including pessimistic
thinking and pessimistic thinkers.
Life is short; the sooner you can laugh at yourself,
the sooner you will be living happily.
Action may not always bring happiness,
but there is no true happiness without action.
If you want to be happy, be happy. Be happy in this moment.
This moment is your life. There is no better time to be happy,
other than now. No medicine cures what happiness can not.
Success is not the key to happiness; happiness is the key to
success. If you are happy doing what you are doing,
you are already successful.
Live for something that is bigger than you are.
Altruism can lead to a happier, more satisfying life,
though not necessarily an easier one.
Don't put the keys to your happiness in someone else's pocket.

MONDAY **1** Bank holiday

Resist the lure of glossy advertising

TUESDAY **2**

Decide what is important to you

Heaven is under our feet as well as over our heads.

Henry David Thoreau

You must understand the whole of life, not just one little part of it. That is why you must read, that is why you must look at the skies, that is why you must sing and dance, and write poems and suffer and understand, for all that is life.

Jiddu Krishnamurti

WEDNESDAY **3**

Learn from the mistakes of others

THURSDAY **4**

Everyone deserves to be heard

FRIDAY **5**

This too will pass

May

There are only two lasting bequests we can hope to give our children. One of these is roots, the other, wings.

Johann Wolfgang von Goethe

There are two basic motivating forces: fear and love. When we fear, we pull back from life. When we love, we open ourselves to all that life has to offer with passion, excitement, and acceptance. We need to learn to love ourselves first, in all our glory and our imperfections. If we cannot love ourselves, we cannot be fully open to our ability to love others. Evolution and all hopes for a better world rest in the fearlessness and open-hearted vision of people who embrace life.

from John Lennon

SEVEN STEPS TO SERENITY

Think less; Reflect more.
Frown less; Smile more.
Talk less; Say more.
Argue less; Listen more.
Judge less; Accept more.
Observe less; Participate more.
Complain less; Appreciate more.
Fear less; Encourage more.

Blessed are the hearts that can bend,
for they shall never be broken.
Albert Camus

My mission in life is not merely to survive, but to thrive; and to do so with some passion, some compassion, some humour, and some style.
Maya Angelou

It's wonderful to know you're aging, because that means you're still on the planet, right?
Goldie Hawn

The nicest thing for me is sleep, then at least I can dream. Beneath the makeup and behind the smile I am just a girl who wishes for the world.
Marilyn Monroe

SATURDAY **6**

Nurture the relationships you have

SUNDAY **7**

Multitasking takes its toll

May

Listen to the woman when she looks at you, not when she talks at you.

Khalil Gibran

A cloudy day is no match for a sunny disposition.

William Arthur Ward

All we demand is our right to twinkle.

MONDAY 8

Give the person you are with your full attention

TUESDAY 9

Be willing to laugh at yourself, and at life

WEDNESDAY 10

Be a good listener

THURSDAY 11

Use your time wisely – this moment will not come again.

> **Adversity is like a strong wind.**
> **It tears away from us all but the**
> **things that cannot be torn, so that**
> **we see ourselves as we really are.**
> *Arthur Golden*

> *Write injuries in sand.*
> *Write kindnesses in marble.*
> *French proverb*

FRIDAY 12

You do not have to prove yourself to anyone

SATURDAY 13

Take time out for yourself every day

SUNDAY 14

Allow for wonder in your life

> **Health is the greatest possession.**
> **Contentment is the greatest treasure.**
> **Confidence is the greatest friend.**
> *Lao Tzu*

May

An apple a day keeps the doctor away.

Delicious apple smoothie

WHAT YOU WILL NEED
Rich in fibre, vitamin C and antioxidants.
½ cup skim or soy milk,
3 tbsp vanilla or plain yoghurt,
1 medium apple peeled and chopped,
2 tbsp cashew butter
3-4 ice cubes

THE HOW-TO PART
Blend for 1 minute until smooth.
Pour it in a glass and enjoy.

MONDAY **15**

Only complain to someone who can do something about it

TUESDAY **16**

Love many things

WEDNESDAY **17**

Think big, aim high, act bold

> *But I know, somehow, that only when it is dark enough can you see the stars.*
>
> Martin Luther King Jr

THURSDAY **18**

Be open to opportunity

FRIDAY **19**

Who's life is it anyway?

SATURDAY **20**

Clear out the clutter

SUNDAY **21**

Get up, dress up and show up

Don't limit your children to your own learning, for they were born for another time.

59

May

The real magic in relationships happens in the absence of judgment of others.

Wayne Dyer

MONDAY **22**

Create good memories

TUESDAY **23**

Get out of your comfort zone

WEDNESDAY **24**

Help someone else succeed

Children are living beings – more living than grown-up people who have built shells of habit around themselves. Therefore it is absolutely necessary for their mental health and development that they should not have mere schools for their lessons, but a world whose guiding spirit is personal love.

Rabindranath Tagore

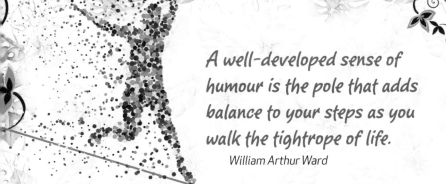

A well-developed sense of humour is the pole that adds balance to your steps as you walk the tightrope of life.

William Arthur Ward

THURSDAY 25

Plan a Girls Night in

FRIDAY 26

Be happy for no reason

Progress is impossible without change, and those who cannot change their minds cannot change anything.

George Bernard Shaw

Home happiness cake

WHAT YOU WILL NEED
1 cup common sense.
1½ cup love sifted with
1½ tsp mutual trust and confidence,
½ cup fairness.
A generous helping of listening.
2 large portions of forgiveness.
1 great big dollop of humour.

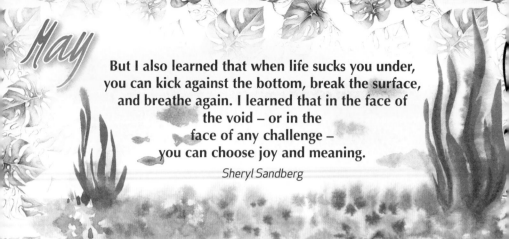

May

But I also learned that when life sucks you under, you can kick against the bottom, break the surface, and breathe again. I learned that in the face of the void – or in the face of any challenge – you can choose joy and meaning.

Sheryl Sandberg

You don't learn to walk by following rules. You learn by doing, and by falling over. One thing is certain in business as in life, you. and everyone around you, will make mistakes.

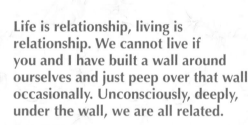

Life is relationship, living is relationship. We cannot live if you and I have built a wall around ourselves and just peep over that wall occasionally. Unconsciously, deeply, under the wall, we are all related.

Jiddu Krishnamurti

SATURDAY **27**

Take positive action

SUNDAY **28**

Turn your can'ts into cans and your won'ts into wills

MONDAY **29**

Stay away from the Cudda Wouda Shudda sisters

TUESDAY **30**

Great questions lead the way to great answers

If we couldn't laugh, we would all go insane.

Jimmy Buffett

There are things I need to tell you, but would you listen if I told you how quickly time passes?
You will awake someday to find that your life has rushed by at a speed at once impossible and cruel.

Enjoy life. There's plenty of time to be dead.

Hans Christian Andersen

Animals are such agreeable friends – they ask no questions, they pass no criticisms.

George Eliot

WEDNESDAY **31**

Be gentle with yourself

BUCKET LIST

for

June

Leadership MONTH

No matter what people tell you, words and ideas can change the world.

Robin Williams

Happiness is like a kiss.
You must share it to enjoy it.

Bernard Meltzer

You are the sum total of everything you've ever seen, heard, eaten, smelled, been told, forgot – it's all there. Everything influences each of us, and because of that I try to make sure that my experiences are positive.

Maya Angelou

The best antidote I know for worry is work. The best cure for weariness is the challenge of helping someone who is even more tired. One of the great ironies of life is this: He or she who serves almost always benefits more than he or she who is served.

Gordon B Hinckley

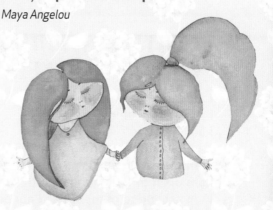

When everyone else leaves you it's loneliness you feel; when you leave everyone else, it's solitude.

Alfred Polgar

Be careful what you water your dreams with. Water them with worry and fear and you will produce weeds that choke the life from your dream. Water them with optimism and solutions and you will cultivate success. Always be on the lookout for ways to turn a problem into an opportunity for success. Always be on the lookout for ways to nurture your dream.

Lao Tzu

THURSDAY **1**

Give the gift of your happiness to your friends and family

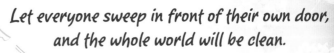

JUNE

Let everyone sweep in front of their own door,
and the whole world will be clean.

Goethe

POSITIVE AFFIRMATIONS FOR A FULFILLED LIFE

I am unique and valuable
I am worthy of love
I am vital and full of energy
I am beautiful and loving and loved
I am safe in the universe
I am open to the abundance that surrounds me
I am accepting of myself as I am accepting of others
I am forgiving so I can be free
I am free to love myself, to love life and to love the world
I am letting go of the past that has limited my future
I am leaving behind all feelings of unworthiness
I am changing thoughts of hurt to words that heal
I am grateful for all that I am and all that I have
I am seeing the beauty that surrounds me
I am acknowledging the beauty that is within me
I express my love for my family and friends
I honour my friendships
I value my relationships
I appreciate my home and my comforts
I respect my body and take good care of it
I smile at the world and the world smiles at me
I love life and life loves me back
I deserve all the goodness that life has to offer
I trust in the process of life
I am doing my best with what I have, where I am
I promise myself I will continue to live the
life that has been gifted to me
I am content
I am satisfied
I am at peace

> *Nothing is so fatiguing as the eternal hanging on of an uncompleted task.*
>
> William James

FRIDAY **2**

Have a mind open to new ideas

SATURDAY **3**

Don't wait – the time will never be just right

SUNDAY **4**

All will be well

> *Live boldly. Laugh loudly. Love truly. Play as often as you can. Work as smart as you are able. Share your heart as deeply as you can reach.*
>
> Mary Anne Radmache

> **Let us be grateful to people who make us happy, they are the charming gardeners who make our souls blossom.**
>
> Marcel Proust

I am no longer accepting the things I cannot change – I'm changing the things I cannot accept.

Angela Davis

MONDAY 5 Bank holiday

Life teaches us to be patient

TUESDAY 6

Respect your body

WEDNESDAY 7

Everything is a little bit strange sometimes

THURSDAY 8

Don't lose sight of what's really important

FRIDAY 9

You do not need permission to be yourself

> *Women are the real architects of society.*
>
> Harriet Beecher Stowe

SATURDAY **10**

Be how you really want to be

SUNDAY **11**

The best way out is always through

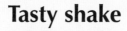

Tasty shake

WHAT YOU WILL NEED
1 cup chilled plain coffee,
1 ½ chopped banana,
1 cup plain yoghurt,
1 tbsp powdered flax seeds,
2 tsp honey,
½ tsp cinnamon powder,
½ tsp nutmeg powder (or grated)
2-3 ice cubes.

THE HOW-TO PART
Blend until the shake gains a smooth consistency.
Add a little more milk or yoghurt if you want to change its texture.

If you bring forth what is within you, what you bring forth will save you. If you do not bring forth what is within you, what you do not bring forth will destroy you.

Saint Thomas

There is wisdom in wonder.

MONDAY 12

Life is full of miracles

TUESDAY 13

Eliminate unwanted distractions

WEDNESDAY 14

For balance, keep it light and flexible

THURSDAY 15

Respect the feelings of others

FRIDAY 16

Look for the win-win option

Never go to bed mad.
Stay up and fight.
Phyllis Diller

SATURDAY **17**

Respond to a negative situation with a positive intent

SUNDAY **18** Father's Day

Break big goals into smaller tasks

Write it on your heart that every day is the best day in the year. He is rich who owns the day, and no one owns the day who allows it to be invaded with fret and anxiety.

True wisdom comes to each of us when we realise how little we understand about life, ourselves, and the world around us.
Socrates

Finish every day and be done with it.
You have done what you could.
Some blunders and absurdities, no doubt crept in.
Forget them as soon as you can, tomorrow is a new day;
begin it well and serenely, with too high a spirit
to be encumbered with your old nonsense.
Ralph Waldo Emerson

June

Don't limit a child to your own learning, for she was born for another time.

Rabindranath Tagore

This new day is too dear, with its hopes and invitations, to waste a moment on the yesterdays.

Ralph Waldo Emerson

Nothing in life is to be feared, it is only to be understood. Now is the time to understand more, so that we may fear less.

Marie Curie

MONDAY **19**

There is an upside to every situation

TUESDAY **20**

Schedule regular downtime

WEDNESDAY **21**

Keep everything in perspective

THURSDAY **22**

We become like the people we regularly associate with

Whenever two people meet, there are really six people present. There is each as he sees himself, each as the other person sees him, and each as he really is.

William James

Facts are only as interesting as the possibilities they open up to the imagination.

The truth will set you free ... but first it will piss you off!

FRIDAY 23

Do more of what you love

SATURDAY 24

We are empowered by empowering others

SUNDAY 25

Have people in your life who make you laugh

JUNE

The most effective people are those who are the best at asking for what they want.

MONDAY **26**

Stand up for what is right

TUESDAY **27**

Value your unique contribution

WEDNESDAY **28**

Love your life

THURSDAY **29**

Stop waiting for the world to make you happy – it's a DIY job

FRIDAY **30**

Enjoy the fruits of a healthy lifestyle

BUCKET LIST
for
July

Inspiration MONTH
(and fun)

_____

_____

_____

_____

_____

_____

_____

_____

_____

_____

_____

_____

_____

Your attitude is like a box of crayons that colour your world. Constantly colour your picture grey, and your picture will always be bleak. Try adding some bright colours to the picture by including humour, and fun, and your picture begins to lighten and brighten.

It's a good day to have a good day.

Keep your face to the sunshine and you cannot see a shadow.
Helen Keller

Don't let rejection create self-doubt.

MUD PUDDLES AND DANDELIONS

When I look at a patch of dandelions, I see a bunch of weeds that are going to take over my garden. My children see pretty flowers for mummy and blowing stuff you can make wishes on. When I look at an old drunk and he smiles at me, I see a smelly, dirty person who wants money and I look away.

My children see a kindly old man smiling at them and they smile right back.

When I hear music I love, I'm aware I can't carry a tune or have much rhythm so I listen quietly and self consciously, and maybe tap my foot.

My children feel the beat and jump around freely with it. They sing out the words and if they don't know the words, they make up their own.

When I feel the wind on my face, I brace myself against it. I complain it's messing up my hair and making it difficult for me when I walk.

My children close their eyes, spread their arms and fly with it until they fall on the ground laughing.

When I pray I say 'Thee' and 'Thou' and 'Grant me' this and 'Give me' that.

My children say "Hi God. Thank you for my toys and my friends. Please keep the bad dreams away tonight. Sorry, I don't want to go to heaven yet. I would miss mummy and daddy too much".

When I see a mud puddle I step around it. I see muddy shoes and dirty carpets.

My children sit in it. They see dams to build, rivers to cross and worms to play with.

When did we decide we had to be so grown up and sensible?

I wonder if we are given little children to teach, or to learn from.

Enjoy the little things in life, for one day, you will look back and realise they were the big things.

I wish you mud puddles and dandelions.

SATURDAY 1

Have the strength to try again

SUNDAY 2

Learn to experience and appreciate the present moment

> If there is light in the soul, there
> will be beauty in the person.
> If there is beauty in the person, there
> will be harmony in the house.
> *Chinese proverb*

MONDAY **3**

Welcome the unexpected

> **Your living is determined
> not so much by what life brings to
> you as by the attitude you bring to
> life; not so much by what happens
> to you as by the way your mind
> looks at what happens.**
> *Khalil Glibran*

TUESDAY **4**

Pay attention to what matters most

WEDNESDAY **5**

Don't talk yourself down – unless you're on a ladder

July

A PARENT'S PRAYER
Please help me
To strengthen their voices, bodies and minds
To express their feelings and control them sometimes
To explore what's near
And venture afar
And most important
To love who they are.

*We must be willing to let go of the life we've planned,
so as to have the life that is waiting for us.*

Joseph Campbell

THURSDAY 6

Failure is a word used by losers

FRIDAY 7

Don't limit your challenges, challenge your limits

SATURDAY 8

Resist trying to justify yourself – there is no need

SUNDAY 9

Face the future with courage and confidence

Just take any step, whether small or large. And then another, and another, day after day. It may take months, maybe years, but as you choose your steps the path to your destination becomes clear. Be sure to notice the flowers scattered along the way.

Aaron Ross

MONDAY **10**

Explore the limits of your comfort zone

TUESDAY **11**

Opinions are interesting but they are not facts

WEDNESDAY **12**

Feel the fear and do it anyway

THURSDAY **13**

Stretch the barriers to your thinking

JULY

Man does not control his own fate.
The women in his life do that for him.

Groucho Marx

FRIDAY 14

Choose your friends carefully

SATURDAY 15

You are responsible for your own journey

SUNDAY 16

Sort out your priorities

Time decides who you meet in your life.
Your heart decides who you want in your life.
Your behaviour decides who stays in your life.

Forgive and forget.
Forgiving wins perspective .
Forgetting wins friends.

To let go is to release the images and emotions, the grudges and fears, the clingings and disappointments of the past, that bind our spirit.

Jack Kornfield

MONDAY 17

Get rid of excuses

You will never be sorry:
For thinking before acting,
For listening before judging,
For forgiving your enemies,
For helping your friends,
For being candid and frank,
For standing by your principles,
For honouring your word,
For playing full out,
For being kind and courteous,
For being loving and forgiving,
For trusting your faith,
For doing your best.

When people tell me "you're going to regret that in the morning", I sleep until noon.

TUESDAY 18

Look for the solution in every challenge

If you want to sacrifice the admiration of many men for the criticism of one, go ahead – get married!

Katherine Hepburn.

WEDNESDAY **19**

What would someone you admire do in this situation?

THURSDAY **20**

Don't look back, you're not going that way

FRIDAY **21**

Criticism gets you nowhere

SATURDAY **22**

When principle is involved, don't budge

SUNDAY **23**

Avoid making assumptions

> Life was meant to be lived, and curiosity must be kept alive. One must never, for whatever reason, turn one's back on life.
>
> *Eleanor Roosevelt*

MONDAY 24

Find the who that knows the how

TUESDAY 25

How you view the world is your choice

WEDNESDAY 26

Let your love be seen in your smile

> *People will forget what you said, people will forget what you did, but people will never forget how you made them feel.*
>
> *Maya Angelou*

WISE WAYS TO **WELLBEING**

Invest in your overall health and happiness. It's important.
Pay attention to your thoughts and feelings – but remember they're fickle!
Acknowledge your resilience in the face of challenges.
Find new ways to express your creativity.
Understand the importance of social connections.
Recognise the power and inspiration of spirituality.
Discover the value of staying positive.
Enjoy spending time with yourself.
Allow others to contribute.
Nurture your friendships
Engage with your surroundings.
Let go feeling guilty about anything.
Indulge yourself with random pamper days.
Talk out feelings of stress and watch them dissolve.
Be kind – do nice things.
Breathe. When your mind is frazzled take 10 deep breaths. It grounds you.
Practice daily meditation to bring peace of mind and relaxation of body.
Be happy – it goes a long way in nurturing your being well.

Silence is the presence of time undisturbed.

*We are afraid to care too much,
for fear that the other person
does not care at all.*

Eleanor Roosevelt

THURSDAY 27

Take small steps in the direction you want to go

FRIDAY 28

Listen to those who love you

**To be mature you have to realise what you value most.
Not to arrive at a clear understanding of one's own values
is a tragic waste. You have missed the whole
point of what life is for.**

Eleanor Roosevelt

SATURDAY 29

To make your parents happy, just be happy

SUNDAY 30

Plan a picnic in a local beauty spot

It's madness...

...to hate all roses
because you got scratched with one thorn,

...to give up all dreams
because one of them didn't come true,

...to give up all attempts
because one of them failed.

It's folly to condemn all your friends
because one has betrayed you,
to no longer believe in love
just because someone was unfaithful
or didn't love you back,
to throw away all your chances to be happy
because something went wrong.

There will always be another opportunity,
another friend, another love, a new strength.

For every end, there is always a new beginning.

And now here is my secret, a very simple secret:

It is only with the heart that one can see rightly;
what is essential is invisible to the eye.

Antoine de Saint-Exupéry, The Little Prince

MONDAY **31**

Every problem has a solution

BUCKET LIST
for
August

Curiosity MONTH

_____
_____
_____
_____
_____
_____
_____
_____
_____
_____
_____
_____
_____
_____

Life was meant to be lived,
and curiosity must be kept alive.
Eleanor Roosevelt

One child, one teacher, one pen, and
one book can change the world.
Malala Yousafzai

Without leaps of imagination or dreaming, we
lose the excitement of possibilities. Dreaming,
after all, is a form of planning.
Gloria Steinem.

August

And, of course men know best about everything, except what women know better.

George Eliot

TUESDAY **1**

What you do makes a difference

WEDNESDAY **2**

Be willing to be brave

It took me quite a long time to develop a voice, and now that I have it, I am not going to be silent.

Madeleine Albright

The world is incomprehensible. We won't ever understand it; we won't ever unravel its secrets. Thus we must treat the world as it is: a sheer mystery.

Carlos Castaneda

A strong positive mental attitude will create more miracles than any wonder drug.

Patricia Neal

When you are happy, you enjoy the music. When you are sad, you understand the lyrics.

SIMPLE RITUALS FOR SELF CARE

Schedule regular events with family and friends.

Practice mindfulness. Be present wherever you are. Experience every moment in its entirety – every occasion, location and conversation.

Exercise. It protects physical and emotional health, relieves stress, and makes you feel good. It's moving that matters.

Spend some time outside. Notice as colour and scenery changes around you – the lights, the smells, feel your feet on the ground. Sunlight is a great natural way to boost your mood.

Deal with your emotions. Learn how to deal responsibly with stress, anger, upset and anxiety instead of keeping them bottled up inside. Dialogue beats monologue every time! Reach out. Speak out.

Be healthy inside. Avoid junk food and stick to a healthy diet. Steer clear of smoking, drug use, and too much alcohol. Learn to cook healthy meals with real food.

Treat your senses. Do little things like lighting a scented candle, buying some fresh-cut flowers, indulging in a massage or treating yourself to lunch with your favourite friends. Stop and smell the roses – regularly!

Discover the benefits of gentle yoga. The focus is on who/how you are 'being' in your body rather than what you are 'doing' with your body. And notice how flexible you are.

Sleep. Everyone gets cranky without enough sleep, so dedicate adequate sleep time every night. Let your mind wind down … and sink into peaceful rest.

Keep a Gratitude Journal. This gives you an opportunity for reflection. Fill your gratitude journal with joyful encounters and special moments of connection, focusing on the happy bits. Perfection doesn't exist, but there is always something to be grateful for.

Make happiness a priority. Allow yourself to laugh and have fun. Let young people see that 'grown-ups' have a great life and adulthood is full of exciting possibilities.

Destroying rainforest for economic gain is like burning a Renaissance painting to cook a meal.

EO Wilson

Spinach salad

WHAT YOU WILL NEED
1-2 bunches of spinach – washed, dried and torn into bite size pieces
I cup fresh mushrooms thinly sliced.
½ red onion thinly sliced and separated into rings
2 hardboiled eggs – chopped
6 slices bacon – cooked crisp and crumbled.

DRESSING
Dress with
A friend's (delicious) salad dressing
½ cup oil
1 teaspoon salt
I teaspoon Worcestershire sauce
I teaspoon horseradish
I garlic clove
3 tablespoons vinegar
Dash of Tabasco sauce (careful)
Ground pepper to taste
Combine all ingredients – shake well – allow to stand several hours.
Remove garlic clove before serving.

Or
Sweet vinaigrette dressing
½ teaspoon salt
¼ teaspoon freshly ground pepper
2 tablespoons sugar or honey
1 teaspoon Dijon mustard or ¼ teaspoon dry mustard
2 tablespoons wine vinegar or lemon juice
½ cup oil
Whisk all ingredients except oil until dissolved.
Add oil and shake in a covered jar.
Toss with salad.

I'm an introvert... I love being by myself, love being outdoors, love taking a long walk with my dogs and looking at the trees, flowers, the sky.

Audrey Hepburn

THURSDAY **3**

Be the bridge

> *Better do a good deed near at home*
> *than go far away to burn incense.*
>
> *Amelia Earhart*

> ***We all require and want respect, man or woman,***
> ***black or white. It's our basic human right.***
>
> *Arethra Franklin*

FRIDAY **4**

Simplify your life

SATURDAY **5**

Look for the inner beauty in people

> *It's our outlook on life that counts. If we take ourselves lightly*
> *and don't take ourselves too seriously, pretty soon we can find the*
> *humour in our everyday lives. And sometimes it can be a lifesaver.*
>
> *Betty White*

> **Vulnerability is about showing up and being**
> **seen. It's tough to do that when we're terrified**
> **about what people might see or think.**
>
> *Brené Brown*

SUNDAY **6**

Take time for you

August

> It takes a lot of courage to show your dreams to someone else.
> *Erma Bombeck*

> *Paradoxical as it may seem, to believe in youth is to look backward; to look forward we must believe in age.*
> *Dorothy L Sayers*

MONDAY 7 Bank holiday

Allow yourself a good cry

TUESDAY 8

Let go of the past

WEDNESDAY 9

Expand your mind with new ideas

THURSDAY 10

Sometimes you just need to let go the need to be perfect

> *Old age is no place for sissies.*
> Bette Davis

FRIDAY 11

Find a meaningful way to give back

SATURDAY 12

Embrace friendship

> When humour goes out the window, civilization follows!

> *One cannot think well, love well, sleep well, if one has not dined well.*
> Virginia Woolf

It is not until you become a mother that your judgment slowly turns to compassion and understanding.
Erma Bombeck

Understanding is a two-way street.
Eleanor Roosevelt

SUNDAY 13

Congratulate yourself on your achievements

August

There are people who have money and people who are rich.

Coco Chanel

MONDAY **14**

Help others to help themselves

TUESDAY **15**

Fill your mind with pleasant thoughts

WEDNESDAY **16**

Prepare to get a good night's sleep

The soul should always stand ajar, ready to welcome the ecstatic experience.

Emily Dickinson

THURSDAY **17**

Compassion and kindness work wonders

There's something liberating about not pretending. Dare to embarrass yourself. Risk.

Drew Barrymore

All growth is a leap in the dark.

Henry Millar

In nature, nothing is perfect and everything is perfect. Trees can be contorted, bent in weird ways, and they're still beautiful.

Alice Walker

FRIDAY **18**

Do what you know to be the right thing

SATURDAY **19**

Forgive an old friend

SUNDAY **20**

All blame is a waste of time

August

If you can't fly, then run. If you can't run, then walk. If you can't walk, then crawl. But whateve you do, you have to keep moving forward.

Martin Luther King Jr

In the end, we only regret the chances we didn't take, the relationships we were afraid to have, and the decisions we waited too long to make.

Lewis Carroll

MONDAY 21

Let go of the baggage that weighs you down

TUESDAY 22

See the world through grateful eyes

WEDNESDAY 23

The work will only get done in the doing of it

THURSDAY 24

Be at peace with who you are

It's like if you don't go to a dance you can never be rejected, but you'll never get to dance either.

Maeve Binchy

Try to be a rainbow in someone's cloud.

Maya Angelou

If you don't like the road you're walking, start paving another one.

Dolly Parton

FRIDAY 25

Everything can change in the blink of an eye

SATURDAY 26

Don't fear the future

SUNDAY 27

Everyone deserves to be heard, so listen!

> *When you accept change, let go, and free yourself*
> *from fear of the unknown, you will begin to see*
> *your life as an exciting adventure.*
> Joe Keane

MONDAY **28**

Keep focused on what you want to achieve

TUESDAY **29**

Do not make yourself indispensable

WEDNESDAY **30**

Every day is a new chance to start again

> **You've done it before and you can do it now. See the positive possibilities. Redirect the substantial energy of your frustration and turn it into positive, effective, unstoppable determination.**
> Ralph Marston

THURSDAY **31**

Peace begins in your own heart

BUCKET LIST

for

September

Gratitudue MONTH

Think as little as possible about yourself. Think as much as possible about other people.

Eleanor Roosevelt

Some people grumble that roses have thorns. I am grateful that thorns have roses.

Alphonsus Karr

Each of us has cause to think with deep gratitude of those who have lighted the flame within us.

Albert Schweitzer

Gratitude as a discipline involves a conscious choice. I can choose to be grateful even when my emotions and feelings are still steeped in hurt and resentment. It is amazing how many occasions present themselves in which I can choose gratitude instead of a complaint. I can choose to be grateful when I am criticised, even when my heart still responds in bitterness. I can choose to speak about goodness and beauty, even when my inner eye still looks for someone to accuse or something to call ugly.

Henri JM Nouwen

September

> As we express our gratitude, we must never forget that the highest appreciation is not to utter words, but to live by them.
>
> *John F Kennedy*

Life is abundant, and life is beautiful. And it's a good place that we're all in, you know, on this earth, if we take care of it.

Alice Walker

One loyal friend is worth ten thousand relatives.

Euripides

FRIDAY **1**

Love yourself just the way you are

SATURDAY **2**

Life teaches us to be patient

SUNDAY **3**

Worry causes wrinkles

gratitude

GRATITUDE GUIDE
I am grateful for:

A personal strength _____

A family trait that inspires me _____

A skill I have learned _____

A natural talent I have _____

A unique feature about me _____

Something I have that money couldn't buy _____

An opportunity I was offered . _____

A relationship I have _____

The health I have _____

An interesting discovery that I made _____

A choice I made _____

A risk I took _____

A result I achieved _____

A contribution I made _____

A special gift I received _____

A special friend _____

A memory I cherish _____

I person I met _____

A change I made _____

A lesson I learned _____

Gratitude can transform common days into thanksgivings, turn routine jobs into joy, and change ordinary opportunities into blessings.

William Arthur Ward

September

MONDAY **4**

Walk the dog

TUESDAY **5**

Hindsight is great but the best sight is insight

WEDNESDAY **6**

Life is an adventure – be adventurous

THURSDAY **7**

Avoid making comparisons

FRIDAY **8**

Don't gossip

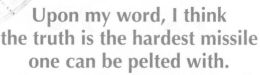

> Upon my word, I think
> the truth is the hardest missile
> one can be pelted with.
>
> *George Eliot*

Fast chicken curry

WHAT YOU WILL NEED
6-8 half breasts of chicken –
skinned and boned.
¼ cup butter
½ cup honey
¼ cup Dijon mustard
2 tablespoons prepared
(jar/squeeze bottle) mustard
of your choice.
1 table spoon curry powder
½ lime – juice and rind, finely
grated.
1 teaspoon salt
1 clove garlic

THE HOW-TO PART
Preheat oven to 180
Arrange chicken in a single
layer in baking dish.
In a saucepan, combine
remaining ingredients and
bring to boil.
Pour over chicken breasts.
Bake for 45 mins, basting
occasionally.
Serve hot or cold.

SATURDAY 9

Tackle your problems head on

SUNDAY 10

Have a bigger why.

September

MONDAY 11

Be proud of your game

TUESDAY 12

The universe is unfolding exactly as it should

*Every great dream begins with a dreamer.
Always remember, you have within you the
strength, the patience, and the passion to reach
for the stars to change the world.*
Harriet Tubman

May your choices reflect your hopes,
not your fears.
Nelson Mandela

WEDNESDAY 13

Encourage the dreams of others

The greatest discovery of all time is that a person can change their future by merely changing their attitude.
Oprah Winfrey

THURSDAY **14**

Do what you know to do

FRIDAY **15**

Complaining is unproductive

SATURDAY **16**

Take it one day at a time

SUNDAY **17**

Be prepared for surprises

September

You have to accept whatever comes, and the only important thing is that you meet it with the best you have to give.

Eleanor Roosevelt

MONDAY **18**

Thinking doesn't change anything

TUESDAY **19**

Write in your journal

WEDNESDAY **20**

Stay open and curious

If you have no one, you are poor;
if you have an acquaintance, you are fortunate;
if you have a friend, you are privileged;
if you have a lover, you are rich;
if you have a soulmate, you are wealthy.

Matshona Dhliwayo

The secret of change is to focus all of
your energy not on fighting the old,
but on building the new.

Socrates

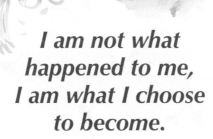

*I am not what
happened to me,
I am what I choose
to become.*

THURSDAY 21

Do not be afraid to fail

FRIDAY 22

Re-experience happy memories

SATURDAY 23

Success does not require misery

SUNDAY 24

Create a life worth loving

September

The future belongs to those who believe in the beauty of their dreams.
Eleanor Roosevelt

MONDAY 25

Your best contribution is a good mood

TUESDAY 26

Don't over-dramatize your life.

WEDNESDAY 27

Let failure point you to success

THURSDAY 28

90%of those who fail are not defeated – they quit

FRIDAY 29

Develop the talent you have

THE GIFT OF **GRATITUDE**

I give thanks for each exquisite moment.
I see and appreciate the light in everyone, including myself.
I am grateful to the universe for manifesting all the
wonderful things in my life so far.
I am grateful for every blessing, no matter how small.
I am grateful for the opportunity to learn, develop, and grow.
I am grateful for all the love in my life – given and received.
I am grateful for the light I see in others, even when it's just a tiny spark.
I am grateful for all the things my physical body allows me to do.
I am grateful for those who show me patience, kindness, and playfulness.
I am grateful for my mistakes because they have made me stronger.
I am grateful that I have access to nourishing food and clean water.
I am grateful for all of the people involved in bringing
wholesome food to my table.
I am grateful for the wisdom of others.
I am grateful for the gift of this one precious human life.
I am grateful for the love and contribution of my unique family.
I am grateful for each and every one of my friends who enrich
my life beyond measure.
I am grateful for the comfort and unconditional love of my pets.
I am grateful for the world around me that connects me with every day.
With gratitude, I see the world in a new light.
With gratitude, I appreciate each day is an opportunity and a gift.
With gratitude, I acknowledge all the blessings I have been bestowed.
With gratitude, I appreciate my strength and resilience.
With gratitude, I value all the obstacles
I had to overcome to get to where I am.
With gratitude, I honour every teacher who
has shaped me into the person I am today.
With gratitude for all that I have now, I embrace
my hopes and dreams for the future.
With gratitude, I accept my unique creativity
and my capacity to enrich other people's lives.
I am grateful for my sense of gratitude – and understanding
it is the way to peace, contentment and a life of abundant joy.

SATURDAY 30

Talk it over with someone you trust

BUCKET LIST
for
October
###
Kindness MONTH

You cannot do a kindness too soon, for you never know how soon it will be too late.

Ralph Waldo Emerson

The smallest actual good is better than the most magnificent promises of possibilities.
Thomas Macauley

Lots of people limit their possibilities by giving up easily. Never tell yourself "this is too much for me" or "it's no use; I can't go on". If you do, you are defeated – by your own thinking! Keep believing and keep on keeping on.

Norman Vincent Peale.

12 THINGS EVERY BUSY WOMAN NEEDS TO LEARN HOW TO DO

PLAN YOUR IDEAL FUTURE: If you really want to succeed in life, the very first step is ask yourself what you really want and write it down. It's your future. Set your compass to your north star.

DO THINGS THAT SCARE YOU: If what you wanted could be found in your comfort zone, you'd already have it.

PRACTICE IN PUBLIC: Have the courage to be public and connect with the people who can help you get what you want.

SPEND LESS THAN YOU EARN AND INVEST THE DIFFERENCE: There's three parts to this: spend less, earn more, and invest wisely. Invest in your growth and development … and see the difference.

DEVELOP HEALTHY MOVEMENT HABITS: Your body was made to move, so start moving. If you don't use it, you might lose it.

DEVELOP HEALTHY EATING HABITS:
High quality = *real food* = meat, vegetables, legumes, fruit, dairy, eggs.
Low quality = *processed food* = nearly anything that comes in a box or a jar.

BECOME INSANELY CURIOUS: Following your curiosity leads to intrinsic motivation – you really want to be doing what you're doing. Extrinsic motivation like money and fame only gets you so far.

MASTER THE ART OF REST: Rest enables work, and work gives meaning to rest. Go for a walk. Sit and think. Pull out a journal and write down your thoughts. Your work will thank you.

LEARN HOW TO LISTEN: Lean in – with attentiveness and interest. Make eye contact – see the other person's face, pay attention to the other person's eyes. Relax – be open to the conversation.

SEEK TO UNDERSTAND: In conversation, you're not just looking for information, you're looking to connect.

BECOME A LIFELONG LEARNER: You're either growing or you're dying. Listen to podcasts while doing something else. Read books. Investing a few hours of attention can give you the best insights from decades of learning.

LEARN TO LAUGH AT YOURSELF.

SUNDAY **1**

Practice enthusiasm and watch your results improve miraculously

October

You are under no obligation to manage the universe.

MONDAY 2

Trust yourself to know who to trust

The truth is the kindest thing we can give folks in the end.
Harriet Beecher Stowe

TUESDAY 3

Getting your own way isn't always winning

WEDNESDAY 4

Don't indulge in gossip

THURSDAY 5

Quit looking back, you're not going that way

> If all misfortunes were laid in one common heap, whence everyone must take an equal portion, most people would be contented to take their own and depart.
>
> *Socrates*

FRIDAY **6**

The only time you have is now

SATURDAY **7**

Learn what there is to learn and move on

SUNDAY **8**

Procrastination is the thief of time

Every day the clock resets. Your wins don't matter. Your failures don't matter. Don't stress on what was, fight for what could be.

Sean Higgins

 **October**

It is not fair to ask of others what you are not willing to do yourself.

Eleanor Roosevelt

MONDAY **9**

Turn off the noise and be with life

TUESDAY **10**

Make amends

WEDNESDAY **11**

Be secure in your values

LESSONS MY MOTHER TAUGHT ME

Give people more than they expect and do it cheerfully.

Never laugh at anyone's dreams. People who don't have dreams don't have much.

Great love and great achievements involve great risk. Be brave.

Remember the 3 R's: Respect for self, Respect for others, Responsibility for all your actions.

Smile when picking up the phone. The caller can hear it in your voice.

When you lose, don't lose the lesson. There is always something to learn.

Life isn't fair, but it is good. Enjoy it as best you can. It's short.

When you say 'I love you" mean it.

Marry someone you like to talk to. When you get older their conversational skills will be as important as any other.

Everything works out for the best in the end.

Prejudice is the child of ignorance.

THURSDAY 12

Mind your own business

FRIDAY 13

Take time out to play

SATURDAY 14

Plan a girls' night out

SUNDAY 15

Value your wellbeing above all else

Children move stones with their feet.
Men move rocks with their hands.
Women move mountains with their hearts.

Matshona Dhliwayo

October

You can often change your circumstances by changing your attitude.

Eleanor Roosevelt

MONDAY **16**

Ask the universe for advice

TUESDAY **17**

Phone an old friend for a good chin-wag

WEDNESDAY **18**

Courage and confidence grow from within

THURSDAY **19**

Face your fears and take action

FRIDAY **20**

Maturity is being at peace with imperfection

The one thing you can give and still keep is your word.

SATURDAY 21

Every problem has a solution

SUNDAY 22

Add value wherever you are

HEALTHY LIFESTYLE
**Good nourishing food.
Balanced diet.
Regular exercise.
Good habits.
Responsible choices.
Rest and relaxation.
Everything in moderation.
Harmonious relationships.
A good night's sleep.**

October

MONDAY **23**

Feedback is the breakfast of champions

TUESDAY **24**

Accept compliments graciously and gracefully

WEDNESDAY **25**

Self expression is essential to life

THURSDAY **26**

Take what you do seriously but yourself lightly

Love can often be misguided and do as much harm as good, but respect can do only good. It assumes that the other person's stature is as large as one's own, his rights as reasonable, his needs as important.

Eleanor Roosevelt,

Confound you handsome young fellows! You think of having it all your own way in the world. You don't understand women. They don't admire you half so much as you admire yourselves.

George Eliot

FRIDAY **27**

Go for a long walk and enjoy the scenery on the way

SATURDAY **28**

Be comfortable with growing older

SUNDAY **29**

Every failure brings with it the seed of an equivalent success

There are people who have money and there are people who are rich.

Coco Chanel.

October

What could we accomplish if we knew we could not fail?

Eleanor Roosevelt

MONDAY 30 Bank holiday

Share the best of you

TUESDAY 31

Give up any destructive habits

I like living. I have sometimes been wildly, despairingly, acutely miserable, racked with sorrow; but through it all I still know quite certainly that just to be alive is a grand thing.

Agatha Christie

Trust that now is always a good time to act.

Trust that the results of taking action are always worth it.

Letting go isn't about having the courage to release the past; it's about having the wisdom to embrace the present.

Steve Maraboli

BUCKET LIST
for
November

Wisdom MONTH

It is unwise to be too sure of ones own wisdom.

Mahatma Gandhi

The truth is rarely pure and never simple.

Oscar Wilde

For beautiful eyes, look for the good in others; for beautiful lips, speak only words of kindness; and for poise, walk with the knowledge that you are never alone.

Audrey Hepburn

November

"Grandma how do you deal with pain?"
"With your hands, dear. When you do it with your mind, the pain hardens even more."
"With your hands, grandma?"
"Yes, yes. Our hands are the antennas of our Soul. When you move them by sewing, cooking, painting, touching the earth or sinking them into the earth, they send signals of caring to the deepest part of you and your Soul calms down. This way she doesn't have to send pain anymore to show it.
"Are hands really that important?"
"Yes my girl. Think of babies: they get to know the world thanks to their touch.
When you look at the hands of older people, they tell more about their lives than any other part of the body.
Everything that is made by hand, so it is said, is made with the heart because it really is like this: hands and heart are connected.
Think of lovers: When their hands touch, they love each other in the most sublime way."
"My hands grandma... how long since I used them like that!"
"Move them my love, start creating with them and everything in you will move.
The pain will not pass away. But it will be the best masterpiece. And it won't hurt as much anymore, because you managed to embroider your Essence."

Elena Barnabé

WEDNESDAY **1**

Design a vision board and 'see' your future

THURSDAY **2**

Figure out what your gifts are and use them

15 CONVERSATION STARTERS

What do you love about your life?
What would you like to change about your life?
What was the happiest time in your life?
What was your most embarrassing moment?
When were you at your lowest ebb?
Who helped you most in your life?
Who inspires you?
If you had a magic wand – what miracle would you wish for?
What gets you out of bed in the morning?
If you had all the money in the world .. what would you do?
What are you most grateful for in your life?
What is your favourite movie and fictional character?
What is your best childhood memory?
Where were you when ....xyz....... happened?
When did you realise all was not quite as it seemed?

FRIDAY **3**

Be the person you want to be

SATURDAY **4**

Take a walk outdoors, sit and enjoy nature

SUNDAY **5**

Be wise about your plans for the future

November

If you desire to know your own being,
Look round at the whole world from every side.
If you truly wish to comprehend the world,
Look into the depths of your own soul.

MONDAY 6

Accept yourself and all that you are

TUESDAY 7

You are unique and valuable

WEDNESDAY 8

Listen to music

THURSDAY 9

Be a role model for others

Follow your bliss and the universe will open doors for
you where there were only walls.

Joseph Campbell

The measure of intelligence is the ability to change.

Albert Einstein

FRIDAY **10**

Deal with any outstanding issues

FUN WAYS TO PERK UP MEALS WITH PEANUT BUTTER

For pork chops: Stir a little milk and a tablespoon of peanut butter into the pan juices and pour over the cooked chops.

For roast chicken or ham: Skim off fat from juices, stir in a little orange juice and a table spoon of peanut butter with the juices. Heat in the pan and pour over chicken/ham.

For chicken salad: Blend peanut butter with mayonnaise.

For creamed vegetables: Add peanut butter to medium white sauce.

For fruit salad/ice-cream/pudding topping: Blend with chocolate syrup or honey.

SATURDAY **11**

Think kind thoughts

SUNDAY **12**

Rid yourself of self- limiting beliefs

November

If we can just let go and trust that things will work out the way they're supposed to, without trying to control the outcome, then we can begin to enjoy the moment more fully. The joy of the freedom it brings becomes more pleasurable than the experience itself.

Goldie Hawn

MONDAY 13

Be inspired to pursue your dreams

TUESDAY 14

Don't wait; the time will never be just right

WEDNESDAY 15

What gets measured gets managed

The education and empowerment of women throughout the world cannot fail to result in a more caring, tolerant, just and peaceful life for all.

Aung San Suu Kyi

A hangover is the wrath of grapes.

THURSDAY **16**

A trade not properly learnt is an enemy

FRIDAY **17**

You are not what you think you are, but what you think... you are'

SATURDAY **18**

Don't let regrets replace your dreams

SUNDAY **19**

Don't worry; be happy

No country can ever truly flourish if it stifles the potential of its women and deprives itself of the contributions of half of its citizens.
Michelle Obama

November

MONDAY **20**

If you want to be loved, be loving

TUESDAY **21**

Your attitude determines your altitude

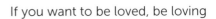

WEDNESDAY **22**

Perhaps what you are looking for is right here

However mean your life is, meet it and live it; do not shun it and call it hard names. It is not so bad. It looks poorest when you are richest. The fault-finder will find faults even in paradise. Love your life, poor as it is. You may perhaps have some pleasant, thrilling, glorious hours, even in a poorhouse. The setting sun is reflected from the windows of the almshouse as brightly as from the rich man's abode; the snow melts before its door as early in the spring. I do not see but a quiet mind may live as contentedly there, and have as cheering thoughts, as in a palace.

Henry David Thoreau

Simple apple cake

WHAT YOU WILL NEED
1 c oil
2 eggs
½ teaspoon salt
4 c apples peeled and sliced
2 c white sugar
2 c flour
1 tsp soda
2 tsp cinnamon
2 tsp vanilla

THE HOW-TO PART
Beat together oil, eggs and salt. Add apples. Add mixture of sugar, flour, soda and cinnamon. Add vanilla. Bake in a 9 x 13 in dish at 350/180 for 45 min

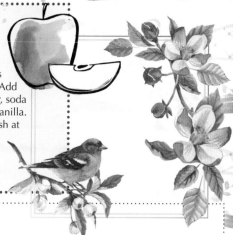

THURSDAY 23

Get into the driving seat of your life

FRIDAY 24

You have excuses or you have results

SATURDAY 25

Set aside time to enjoy your own company

SUNDAY 26

Live up to your own standard and ideals

November

With the new day comes new strength and new thoughts.
Eleanor Roosevelt

Of all the haunting moments of motherhood, few rank with hearing your own words come out of your daughters mouth.
Victoria Secunda

MONDAY 27

Any great structure is built on a strong foundation of integrity

TUESDAY 28

Be clear on what's important to you

WEDNESDAY 29

A good start is half the work

THURSDAY 30

Embrace your own superpowers

CHRISTMAS SHOPPING LIST

1. Buy a 2024 Get Up and Go Diary for all my friends.

2. Buy a Get Up and Go Travel Journal for...

3. Buy a Get Up and Go Young Person's Diary for...

4. Buy a Get Up and Go Daily Planner for Busy Women for...

5. Buy a Get Up and Go Gratitude Journal for...

6. Buy a Get Up and go Leadership Journal for... ...

BUCKET LIST

for

December

Peace MONTH

We must shift our allegiances from fear to curiosity,
from attachment to letting go, from control to trust,
and from entitlement to humility.

Angeles Arrien

SAGE LESSONS ON PEACE

There is no way to peace. Peace is the way.
If you want peace of mind, stop fighting with your thoughts.
Anger is the ultimate destroyer of peace.
We can never obtain peace in the outer world until we
make peace with ourselves.
My heart forgives and releases. Inner peace is my goal.
The life of inner peace, being harmonious and without
stress, is the easiest type of existence.

10 DAYS TO TRANSFORM YOUR LIFE

*Day 1: Get clear on what you REALLY want ...
and why. Write it down.*

*Day 2: Choose a purpose worthy of your life ...
and commit to it.*

*Day 3: Visualise what success looks like for you ...
make a vision board .. and look at it.*

*Day 4: Stop playing the blame game ... it's your life.
No one can live it for you.*

*Day 5: Transform your excuses into actions ...
do what you know to do.*

*Day 6: Celebrate your past accomplishments ...
make a list. You are a capable person.*

*Day 7: Accept 100% responsibility for your life ...
and where you are taking it. (See Day 4)*

*Day 8: Focus on The One Thing you need to change ...
and find a buddy to help you.*

*Day 9: Make room for failure on the road to fulfilment ...
be ready to 'get up and go' again.*

*Day 10: Promise yourself you will not let yourself down.
(Rinse and repeat regularly)*

**The master in the art of living makes little distinction
between his work and his play, his labor and his leisure,
his mind and his body, his information and his recreation,
his love and his religion. He hardly knows which is
which. He simply pursues his vision of excellence at
whatever he does, leaving others to decide whether he is
working or playing. To him he's always doing both.**

James A Michener

December

SHE LET GO

She let go.
Without a thought or a word, she let go.
She let go of fear.
She let go of the judgments.
She let go of the confluence of opinions swarming around her head.
She let go of the committee of indecision within her.
She let go of all the 'right' reasons.
Wholly and completely, without hesitation or worry, she just let go.
She didn't ask anyone for advice. She didn't read a book on how to let go.
She didn't search the scriptures.
She just let go.
She let go of all of the memories that held her back.
She let go of all of the anxiety that kept her from moving forward.
She let go of the planning and all of the calculations about how
to do it just right.
She didn't promise to let go. She didn't journal about it. She didn't write
the projected date in her day-timer. She made no public announcement
and put no ad in the paper. She didn't check the weather report or read
her daily horoscope.
She just let go.
She didn't analyse whether she should let go. She didn't call her friends
to discuss the matter. She didn't do a five-step spiritual mind treatment.
She didn't call the prayer line. She didn't utter one word.
She just let go.
No one was around when it happened. There was no applause or
congratulations. No one thanked her or praised her. No one noticed a
thing. Like a leaf falling from a tree, she just let go.
There was no effort. There was no struggle.
It wasn't good and it wasn't bad. It was what it was,
and it is just that. In the space of letting go, she let it all be.
A small smile came over her face.
A light breeze blew through her.
And the sun and the moon shone forevermore.
Here's to giving ourselves the gift of letting go.
There's only one Guru – you.

Gratitude to the Unknown Artist

134

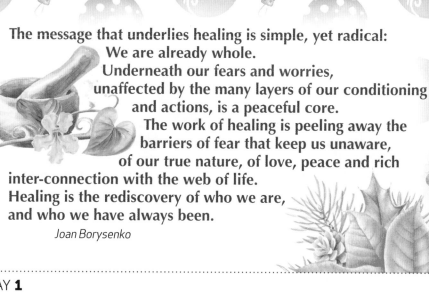

The message that underlies healing is simple, yet radical:
We are already whole.
Underneath our fears and worries,
unaffected by the many layers of our conditioning
and actions, is a peaceful core.
The work of healing is peeling away the
barriers of fear that keep us unaware,
of our true nature, of love, peace and rich
inter-connection with the web of life.
Healing is the rediscovery of who we are,
and who we have always been.

Joan Borysenko

FRIDAY 1

Have a worry-free day

SATURDAY 2

Dance to the beat of your own drum

SUNDAY 3

Listen to your children

*I tell my daughters to have their voice in this world,
and it became clear I needed to role model that.*

Melinda Gates

December

I am no longer waiting for a special occasion;
I burn the best candles on ordinary days.
I am no longer waiting for the house to be clean;
I fill it with people who understand that even dust is sacred.
I am no longer waiting for everyone to understand me;
It's just not their job.
I am no longer waiting for perfect children; our children have
their own beings that burn as brightly as any star.
I am no longer waiting for the other shoe to drop;
It already did, and I'm still here.
I am no longer waiting for the time to be right;
the time is always now.
I am no longer waiting for the mate who will complete me;
I am grateful to be so warmly held by my friends.
I am no longer waiting for that quiet moment;
my mind stills whenever I stop to breathe.
I am no longer waiting for the world to be at peace;
I am at peace and maybe the world will join me.
I am no longer waiting to do something great;
I am doing the small things with great love.
I am no longer waiting to be recognised;
I am visible where I show up.
I am no longer waiting for forgiveness. I forgive.
I am no longer waiting.
I am here.
Now.

*I can shake off everything as
I write; my sorrows disappear,
my courage is reborn.*

Anne Frank

MONDAY **4**

Imagine it possible first

As we grow old, the beauty steals inward.
Ralph Waldo Emerson

TUESDAY 5

The enemy of creativity is self-doubt

Some of us think holding on makes us strong, but sometimes it is letting go.
Hermann Hesse

Attachment leads to jealousy. The shadow of greed, that is. Train yourself to let go of the things you fear to lose.
Yoda

WEDNESDAY 6

Be enthusiastic

THURSDAY 7

Acknowledge those who support you

December

Drink your tea slowly and reverently, as if it is the axis on which the world earth revolves – slowly, evenly, without rushing toward the future; live the actual moment. Only this moment is life.
Thich Nhat Hanh

Just don't give up trying to do what you really want to do. Where there is love and inspiration, I don't think you can go wrong.
Ella Fitzgerald

FRIDAY **8**

Get enough sleep

SATURDAY **9**

Do not compare yourself to others

SUNDAY **10**

Make new friends

The truth is the truth even if no one believes it. A lie is a lie, even if everyone believes it.

MONDAY 11

Every choice you make is a turn your life takes

People have a hard time letting go of their suffering. Out of a fear of the unknown, they prefer suffering that is familiar.
Thich Nhat Hanh

TUESDAY 12

Remember, it's always personal

WEDNESDAY 13

Be great in small things

THURSDAY 14

Face the reality of the world with courage

December

Letting go gives us freedom, and freedom is the only condition for happiness. If, in our heart, we still cling to anything – anger, anxiety, or possessions – we cannot be free.

Thich Nhat Hanh

FRIDAY **15**

A great structure requires a strong foundation of integrity

MIGHTY SMALL WORDS

Did is a word of achievement.
Won't is a word of retreat.
Might is a word of bereavement.
Can't is a word of defeat.
Ought is a word of duty.
Try is a word each hour.
Will is a word of beauty.
Can is a word of power.

Times and conditions change so rapidly that we must keep our aim constantly focused on the future.

Walt Disney

SATURDAY **16**

Have a worry free day

SUNDAY **17**

Own your own uniqueness

10 THINGS TO DO EVERY MORNING TO ENSURE YOU HAVE A GREAT DAY

1. MEDITATE: Reflect regularly on your life, what you are grateful for, who is in your life, what you're happy with, what you want, and why you get up every morning.

2. CHECK OUT YOUR NORTH STAR: Yesterday is done. It's now a memory. Today is a gift, a present. Choose a position of strength, courage and optimism with an intention to have today be another day in the direction of fulfilling those dreams on your vision board.

3. PRACTICE POSITIVE SELF-TALK: Remind yourself of how able and capable you are and what you can accomplish. "I can do this." "Today will be a great day." "It's great to be alive." "Everything will be ok."

4. REACH OUT: Be ready to reach out and connect with those around you. Communicate your needs honestly and listen to hear the needs of others. Be compassionate and understanding.

5. SET HEALTHY BOUNDARIES: It's your day. It's your life. You are responsible for your choices, how you behave and what you say. Be clear in what you are willing to do and what you are not.

6. SET GOALS: What do you want to accomplish today? Be clear and focused on how you will spend your time, and how you will reward yourself when you have accomplished your tasks.

7. EXERCISE: There is always time to dance in the kitchen. Maybe you can make time for a spontaneous walk in the park with a friend.

8. CHALLENGE YOURSELF TO BECOME BETTER: Notice what could be holding you back from fully participating in life. You do not have to settle for being stuck. It's ok to be curious ... what if?

9. EMBRACE JOYFUL MOMENTS: Yes. A full day of possible joyful moments ahead – could you sing while doing the dishes, smile at the pile of ironing, laugh at the seriousness of it all?? It's ok to have fun.

10. LOOK FOR THE BEST: Focus on the amazing possibilities that today offers. Seek out the best, in people, in opportunities, in yourself. It hasn't happened yet. Be alert. Expect miracles!

December

TUESDAY **19**

Be your own best friend

Even though you may want to move forward in your life, you may have one foot on the brakes. In order to be free, we must learn how to let go. Release the hurt. Release the fear. Refuse to entertain your old pain. The energy it takes to hang onto the past is holding you back from a new life. What is it you would let go of today?

Mary Manin Morrissey

be awesome today

It's a myth that you can have it all. You can't. And more importantly, I don't think you should want to. It sounds exhausting.

Isla Fisher

WEDNESDAY **20**

Avoid self pity

THURSDAY **21**

Reach out to others- take the first step

> You know, there's nothing damnable about being a strong woman. The world needs strong women. There are a lot of strong women you do not see who are guiding, helping, mothering strong men. They want to remain unseen. It's kind of nice to be able to play a strong woman who is seen.
>
> *Ginger Rogers*

FIVE GOLDEN RULES TO MAKE YOUR LIFE EASIER

1. Do it now.
2. Be prepared well in advance.
3. Work at your own pace.
4. Do not aim for perfection.
5. Sort out your priorities.

FRIDAY 22

Be true to your own heart

SATURDAY 23

Remember ... you always have a choice

SUNDAY 24

Decide this will be the best day ever!

December

When I let go of what I am, I become what I might be.
When I let go of what I have, I receive what I need.

Tao Te Ching

MONDAY **25** Christmas Day

Let yourself daydream

TUESDAY **26** St Stephen's Day

A good book is a great companion

WEDNESDAY **27**

Keep your own house in order

The first step is always the hardest. Whether you're embarking on a journey to achieve a big goal or simply pulling yourself off the couch to go to bed, the first step you take into action is always the most challenging. That's because it's hard to move beyond your comfort zone! Especially when you're stepping into unknown territory and aren't 100% certain of the path that lies ahead. It's takes an intention … to not stay where you are … and then a decision to act … now! It's only through taking intentional action that you will ever discover what you're capable of. The more actions you take the more you grow in confidence as a person and the more chance you have to accomplish something incredible with your life.

It's not only children who grow. Parents do too. As much as we watch to see what our children do with their lives, they are watching us to see what we do with ours. I can't tell my children to reach for the sun. All I can do is reach for it myself and show them how it's done.

Joyce Manyard

*Merry Christmas
Happy New Year*

THURSDAY 28

Let others lead and be content with the light they shine

FRIDAY 29

Take time to reflect and look inward for answers

SATURDAY 30

Allow yourself to be supported

SUNDAY 31 New Year's Eve

Prepare for the next step

When we are in the midst of chaos let go of the need to try and control it. Be awash in it, experience it in that moment, deal with the flow as it comes, surf the wave.

DESIDERATA

Go placidly amid the noise and haste, and remember what peace there may be in silence. As far as possible without surrender be on good terms with all persons. Speak your truth quietly and clearly, and listen to others, even the dull and ignorant; they too have their story.

Avoid loud and aggressive persons, they are vexations to the spirit. If you compare yourself with others, you may become vain and bitter; for always there will be greater and lesser persons than yourself. Enjoy your achievements as well as your plans. Keep interested in your own career, however humble; it is a real possession in the changing fortunes of time. Exercise caution in your business affairs; for the world is full of trickery. But let this not blind you to what virtue there is; many persons strive for high ideals; and everywhere life is full of heroism.

Be yourself. Especially, do not feign affection. Neither be cynical about love; for in the face of all aridity and disenchantment it is perennial as the grass. Take kindly the counsel of the years, gracefully surrendering the things of youth. Nurture strength of spirit to shield you in sudden misfortune. But do not distress yourself with imaginings. Many fears are born of fatigue and loneliness. Beyond a wholesome discipline, be gentle with yourself.

You are a child of the universe, no less than the trees and the stars; you have a right to be here. And whether or not it is clear to you, no doubt the universe is unfolding as it should. Therefore be at peace with God, whatever you conceive Him to be; and whatever your labours and aspirations, in the noisy confusion of life keep peace with your soul. With all its sham, drudgery and broken dreams, it is still a beautiful world. Be cheerful. Strive to be happy.

Max Ehrmann

2024

JANUARY

Sun	Mon	Tue	Wed	Thu	Fri	Sat
	1	2	3	4	5	6
7	8	9	10	11	12	13
14	15	16	17	18	19	20
21	22	23	24	25	26	27
28	29	30	31			

FEBRUARY

Sun	Mon	Tue	Wed	Thu	Fri	Sat
				1	2	3
4	5	6	7	8	9	10
11	12	13	14	15	16	17
18	19	20	21	22	23	24
25	26	27	28	29		

MARCH

Sun	Mon	Tue	Wed	Thu	Fri	Sat
					1	2
3	4	5	6	7	8	9
10	11	12	13	14	15	16
17	18	19	20	21	22	23
24	25	26	27	28	29	30
31						

APRIL

Sun	Mon	Tue	Wed	Thu	Fri	Sat
	1	2	3	4	5	6
7	8	9	10	11	12	13
14	15	16	17	18	19	20
21	22	23	24	25	26	27
28	29	30				

MAY

Sun	Mon	Tue	Wed	Thu	Fri	Sat
			1	2	3	4
5	6	7	8	9	10	11
12	13	14	15	16	17	18
19	20	21	22	23	24	25
26	27	28	29	30	31	

JUNE

Sun	Mon	Tue	Wed	Thu	Fri	Sat
						1
2	3	4	5	6	7	8
9	10	11	12	13	14	15
16	17	18	19	20	21	22
23	24	25	26	27	28	29
30						

JULY

Sun	Mon	Tue	Wed	Thu	Fri	Sat
	1	2	3	4	5	6
7	8	9	10	11	12	13
14	15	16	17	18	19	20
21	22	23	24	25	26	27
28	29	30	31			

AUGUST

Sun	Mon	Tue	Wed	Thu	Fri	Sat
				1	2	3
4	5	6	7	8	9	10
11	12	13	14	15	16	17
18	19	20	21	22	23	24
25	26	27	28	29	30	31

SEPTEMBER

Sun	Mon	Tue	Wed	Thu	Fri	Sat
1	2	3	4	5	6	7
8	9	10	11	12	13	14
15	16	17	18	19	20	21
22	23	24	25	26	27	28
29	30					

OCTOBER

Sun	Mon	Tue	Wed	Thu	Fri	Sat
		1	2	3	4	5
6	7	8	9	10	11	12
13	14	15	16	17	18	19
20	21	22	23	24	25	26
27	28	29	30	31		

NOVEMBER

Sun	Mon	Tue	Wed	Thu	Fri	Sat
					1	2
3	4	5	6	7	8	9
10	11	12	13	14	15	16
17	18	19	20	21	22	23
24	25	26	27	28	29	30

DECEMBER

Sun	Mon	Tue	Wed	Thu	Fri	Sat
1	2	3	4	5	6	7
8	9	10	11	12	13	14
15	16	17	18	19	20	21
22	23	24	25	26	27	28
29	30	31				

FOR MORE COPIES VISIT OUR WEBSITE

www.getupandgodiary.com

OR CONTACT US ON

info@getupandgodiary.com

Get Up and Go

Postal address: **Get Up and Go Publications Ltd, Unit 7A Cornhill Business Park, Ballyshannon, Co Donegal, Ireland F94 C4AA**

- -

For current prices, special offers and postal charges for your region, please refer to the website (www.getupandgodiary.com).

DIRECT ORDER FORM (please complete by ticking boxes)

PLEASE SEND ME:

The Irish Get Up and Go Diary (paperback), €12/£10	Quantity ☐
The Irish Get Up and Go Diary (padded cover), €17.50/£15	Quantity ☐
The Get Up and Go Diary (paperback), €12/£10	Quantity ☐
Get Up and Go Diary for Busy Women (paperback), €12/£10	Quantity ☐
Get Up and Go Diary for Busy Women (padded cover), €17.50/£15	Quantity ☐
Daily Guide to Good Health and Wellbeing (paperback), €15/£13	Quantity ☐
Get Up and Go Gratitude Journal (padded cover), €17.50/£15	Quantity ☐
Get Up and Go Wallplanner (size: A1), €4/£4	Quantity ☐

Total number of copies ☐

We encourage each reader to visit our website (www.getupandgodiary.com) for current prices, other products, special offers and postal charges for region.

I enclose cheque/postal order for (total amount including P+P): _____

Name: _____

Address: _____

Contact phone number: _____   Email: _____

For general enquiries or to pay by credit/debit card, please contact us on 071 9845938 *or* 085 1764297 (office hours).